Meet Pete's Feet

Clive Gifford

Illustrated by Caroline Champion

Say, "Hi!" to Pete. He is ever so sweet.
He is never mean and always smiles at people he meets.
He always says please and thank you, too.

At weekends, Pete likes to help people down his street.
He tidies up garden weeds and sweeps floors for them.
When it is sunny, Pete likes to fish at Wheat Field Stream.

2

But his favourite meal is not fish, it is lean meat with peas.
And if he has a treat, it has to be cheese.

Can you add a letter to the start of each group of letters below, so that they spell the right words to match the picture?

____eas

____eys

____heese

____ate

____ish

____lates

____lock

____eans

3

You see, Pete likes the same
things as many boys.
He loves games with mates
and seeing movies.
He tries to be neat and tidy
in his best green jeans.

Above his knees, Pete
looks like anyone you might meet.
But below the knees,
he makes some people squeal.

"Are those real feet?" some say.
Others ask, "Can I have a feel? Wow, your feet are unreal!"
You see, Pete has big, no,
huge,
no, giant-sized feet!

4

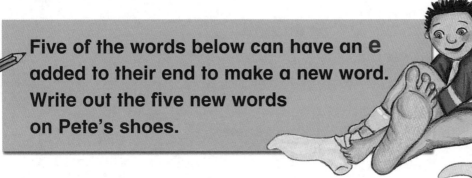

Five of the words below can have an **e** added to their end to make a new word. Write out the five new words on Pete's shoes.

hat   big   not   fin   bin   mat   cut

_____

_____

_____

_____

_____

Pete wrote a letter to his favourite comic.
He was pleased to see his letter in print the next week.
Pete hoped someone would write a letter back.
It would be great to meet someone
who likes big feet.

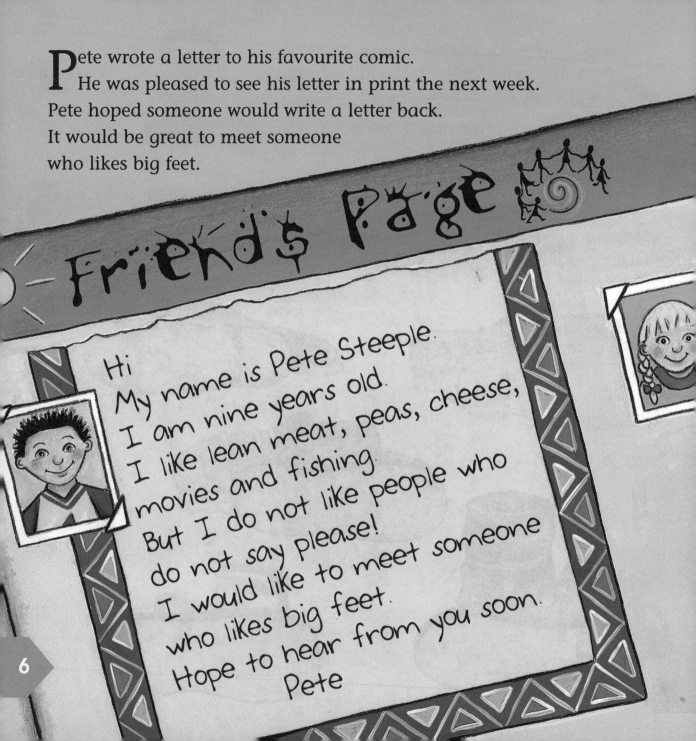

Friend's Page

Hi
My name is Pete Steeple.
I am nine years old.
I like lean meat, peas, cheese,
movies and fishing.
But I do not like people who
do not say please!
I would like to meet someone
who likes big feet.
Hope to hear from you soon.
Pete

Each of the following words are missing a letter. Add an **a** or an **e** to spell the word.

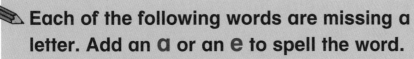

h___n   n___ck

n___me   m___ke

gr___at   ne___t

je___ns   d___ck

A week later, Pete was reading his comic when he saw Kate's letter.
Pete was ever so pleased.

Hello!
I am Kate Blake and I am nine
years old.
I love cheese, movies, cream cakes
and peas.
But I hate people who are late.
I would really like to meet someone
who likes

Kate liked the things he did.
She liked cheese and peas as well as movies.
So Pete and Kate set a date.
They would meet for cakes at the Fine Time Café.

Can you write a letter about yourself just like Kate and Pete wrote for the Friends Page of the weekly comic?

Hello!

- My name is _____.

- I am _____ years old.

- The colour of my hair is _____.

- And the colour of eyes is _____.

- I like _____.

- But I do not like _____.

- I would like to meet _____

_____.

9

Pete walked down the street to the Fine Time Café.
He had to be there by nine. It was half past eight.
He had lots of time. He would not be late.
But then, Pete's feet got stuck in a gate.
And later, they got caught in two milk crates.

"Just great!" sighed Pete.
But he wanted to keep his
date with Kate.

So he ran down the street
with the milk crates still
on his feet.

Pete's wheel spells the word around. Can you work out what the other six word wheels spell? Start with the letter on the red background.

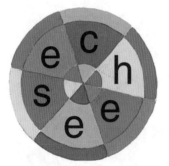

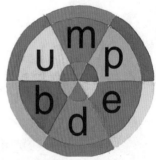

_ _ _ _ _ _ _ _ _ _ _ _ _ _ _

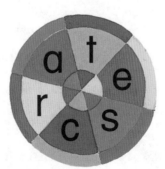

_ _ _ _ _ _ _ _ _ _ _ _ _ _ _

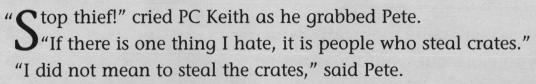

"Stop thief!" cried PC Keith as he grabbed Pete.
"If there is one thing I hate, it is people who steal crates."
"I did not mean to steal the crates," said Pete.
"It's my silly big feet. They get caught in crates and gates."

PC Keith looked at Pete's feet,
"Hmmmm. They are really big.
I see what you mean."

PC Keith helped Pete get the crates
off his feet.
"Thanks, PC Keith," said Pete as he
ran down the street.

my name is pete steeple.
i am nine years old.
i like lean meat, peas, cheese,
movies and fishing.
but i do not like people who
do not say please!
i would like to meet someone
who likes big feet.
hope to hear from you soon.
                    pete

13

Kate was still at the Fine Time Café when Pete got there.
She was about to eat a great big cream cake.

Pete looked at the clock.
It was after nine.
He was late!
He ran over to meet Kate, but his big feet tripped over a table leg.
Pete fell with a yell and hit a stack of plates.
"Don't break my plates!" cried the waiter. It was too late.
The plates hit the floor.

SMASH!

14

nine

real

street

cake

better

great

make

lean

mean

feel

fine

crate

meat

letter

"**S**orry I am late. I am Pete.
May I take a seat?"
But one of Pete's feet was still
stuck round the table leg.
He fell again, this time right into Kate's cake!

SPLOSH!

"That cake took hours to make
and bake," the waiter said.
"S…s…sorry, again," said Pete.
He turned to Kate.
From top to toe, she was covered in cake.
"My bad, mad feet have ruined our date,"
Pete cried.

Here are some pictures of Pete and Kate in different moods. Can you pick the right word to describe each of their moods?

crying   freezing   asleep   shocked
happy   puzzled   ill   sleepy   angry   sad

_____   _____   _____

_____   _____   _____

"Pete, never mind," said Kate. "Have you seen mine?"
"Your cake? I sploshed it all over the place," he replied.
"No, my feet, silly," said Kate. She began to smile.

Pete peeked at Kate's feet.
He could not believe it.

Kate had big feet just like his!

"You see, Pete, the comic did not print who I wanted to meet.
I wanted to meet someone who also has huge feet!"

18

Change the first letter of each of these words to come up with a new word. Read the clues to help you.

deal _____
Clue: food, like breakfast or dinner

free _____
Clue: a big plant with a trunk like an oak or a pine

lake _____
Clue: how you cook bread in an oven

rate _____
Clue: a good friend

lake _____
Clue: a garden tool for clearing leaves

hate _____
Clue: the opposite of early

hose _____
Clue: part of your face

seat _____
Clue: another word for tidy

"Can we meet again?" asked Pete.
He was helping to sweep up all the plates.
"Next time, I promise I will not be late.
And I won't break plates or fall into cakes."

Kate made Pete wait before she said,
"Yes, but next time we will not have cakes.
We will have lean meat and peas and,
maybe, cheese."

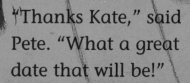

"Thanks Kate," said
Pete. "What a great
date that will be!"

Can you remember the story well enough to write in the missing words?

1 Pete liked to fish at _____ _____ Stream.

2 His favourite meal was _____ meat and _____.

3 Pete and Kate were both _____ years old.

4 Kate's last name was _____.

5 Pete wore _____ jeans.

6 The first thing Pete's feet got stuck in was a _____.

7 PC _____ hated _____ who stole _____.

8 The policeman helped get the _____ off Pete's feet.

9 Pete met Kate at the _____ _____ Café.

10 Kate was about to eat a big _____ _____ before Pete fell into it.

Answers

Page 3

peas   fish
keys   plates
cheese   clock
gate   jeans

Page 5

hat -> hate
not -> note
fin -> fine
mat -> mate
cut -> cute

Page 7

hen   neck
name   make
great   neat
jeans   deck

Page 11

cheese   garden   bumped
people   crates   movies

Page 13

My name is **P**ete **S**teeple.
I am nine years old.
I like lean meat, peas, cheese, movies and fishing.
But **I** do not like people who do not say please!
I would like to meet someone who likes big feet.
Hope to hear from you soon.
Pete

Page 15

street - meat
great - crate
feel - real
letter - better
lean - mean
make - cake
nine - fine

Page 19

meal   rake
tree   late
bake   nose
mate   neat

Page 21

1   Pete liked to fish at **Wheat Field** Stream.
2   His favourite meal was **lean** meat and **peas**.
3   Pete and Kate were both **nine** years old.
4   Kate's last name was **Blake**.
5   Pete wore **green** jeans.
6   The first thing Pete's feet got stuck in was a **gate**.
7   PC **Keith** hated **people** who stole **crates**.
8   The policeman helped get the **crates** off Pete's feet.
9   Pete met Kate at the **Fine Time** Café.
10 Kate was about to eat a big **cream cake** before Pete fell into it.

Page 17

sleepy   ill   happy
angry   shocked sad

Published 2004
10 9 8 7 6 5 4 3 2

Letts Educational, The Chiswick Centre,
414 Chiswick High Road, London W4 5TF
Tel 020 8996 3333   Fax 020 8996 8390
Email mail@lettsed.co.uk
www.letts-education.com

Text, design and illustrations © Letts Educational Ltd 2004

Book Concept, Development and Series Editor:
Helen Jacobs, Publishing Director
Author: Clive Gifford
Book Design: Sandra Perry
Illustrations: Caroline Champion

British Library Cataloguing in Publication Data

A CIP record for this book is available from the British Library.

ISBN 978-1-84315-419-8

Printed in Italy

Colour reproduction by PDQ Digital Media Limited, Bungay, Suffolk